SO-ATZ-950

Los Gatos,

King, Patricia
Mabel the whale.

E
KIN

244

970285 Lakeside Joint School Dist.
19621 Black Road
Los Gatos, Ca. 95030

Santa Clara Valley Library System
Gilroy Public Library
Mountain View Public Library
Santa Clara County Free Library

Alum Rock   Milpitas { Calaveras
Campbell   { Civic Center
Cupertino   { Sunnyhills
Los Altos   Morgan Hill
                 Saratoga { Quito
                          { Village
                 Stanford-Escondido

Central Research Library—Headquarters

For Bookmobile Service, request schedule

THE
FOLLETT
BEGINNING-TO-READ
SERIES

Mabel

Illustrations by Katherine Evans

the Whale

by Patricia King

970285

Santa Clara County Free Library
San Jose, California
Schools Division

Follett Publishing Company   Chicago   New York

Copyright © 1958, by Follett Publishing Company. All rights reserved. No part of this book may be reproduced in any form without written permission from the publisher. Manufactured in the United States of America. Published simultaneously in Canada by The Ryerson Press, Toronto.

 Library of Congress Catalog Card Number: 58-7296

EIGHTH PRINTING   TLA 5443

Mabel was a whale.
She lived in the Pacific Ocean.
The water was very deep.
The water was very blue.

Mabel was a happy whale.
She lived with her cousins.
She played with her cousins.
They swam in the deep blue ocean.

One day some men came.
They came in a ship.
The men caught Mabel.
They did not hurt her.
They put Mabel in the ship.

Then the men took Mabel away
from the deep blue ocean.

They took her to live in a place
called Marineland.

In Marineland fish and sea animals live in big pools or tanks.

People come to see all the fish and sea animals.

Mabel was put into a tank.

The tank was small.

The water was not deep or blue.

The water was not deep at all.

Mabel could not hide in it.

The sun shone down.

It was very hot.

Mabel could not hide her top fin
under the water.

So the hot sun burned Mabel's fin.

People came to see Mabel.

They looked at her through the glass.

The people liked Mabel.

But Mabel did not like the tank.

She did not like the water.

The water was not deep.

Mabel could not hide her top fin
under the water.

Mabel was very unhappy,
and she was very sad.

Her fin hurt.

She lay on the bottom of the tank,
but she could not hide her fin.

The sun still burned it.

Soon Mabel was very sick.

The doctor came to see Mabel.

He looked at her from head to tail.

The doctor saw the sunburned fin.

He knew that fin hurt Mabel.

Then the doctor told the men at
Marineland how to help Mabel.

The men put a cool cream on her fin.

The cool cream was for sunburn.

Then the men put an old bag over the fin.

The sun could not burn through the bag.

It could not hurt the fin now.

But Mabel did not feel any better.
She was still a very unhappy whale.
She even stopped eating.

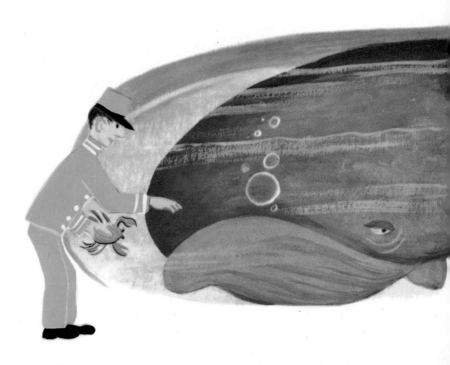

Mabel was very sad.
Everyone wanted to help her.
They thought and thought.
What could they do?

Then the men at Marineland had
an idea.

There was a very big round tank
in Marineland.

If they moved Mabel to the
big tank, she would have more water.

How could they move Mabel?
It would not be easy.
The men thought and thought.

At last the men brought a big,
big crane.

Then they brought many mattresses.
Then they brought a raft.

They put the mattresses on the
raft.

They put Mabel on the mattresses.

Then the men lifted the raft,
the mattresses, and Mabel
with the big, big crane.

They put the raft, the mattresses, and Mabel on a big truck.

The truck moved Mabel to the big tank.

Then Mabel was lifted fifty feet
up into the air with the crane.
She was put into her new big tank.

Then the doctor gave Mabel
some shots.

They were whale-sized shots.

The shots kept Mabel quiet until
she got used to her new tank.

The shots made Mabel feel better.

Then a man walked Mabel around
and around in her new tank.

He walked her around the tank
so she would get to know it.

Soon Mabel felt better.

She swam around her new tank.

The water was deep.

The water covered Mabel's fin.

The sun did not shine on the fin
and burn it.

Mabel was happy.

Before long, Mabel blew!

It was a happy spray.

Mabel was a happy whale.

Everyone at Marineland was happy
because Mabel was well again.

MABEL THE WHALE

Reading Level: Level Two. *Mabel the Whale* has a total vocabulary of 161 words. It has been tested in second grade classes, where it was read with ease.

Uses of this Book: School classes that have an aquarium and children who keep fish or have been to Marineland will be particularly interested in this story, based on a real incident at Marineland. Primarily, however, the book is a story—easy, short, and interesting—which will give beginning readers the experience of reading for fun.

Word List

All of the 161 words used in *Mabel the Whale* are listed. Regular plurals (-*s*) and regular verb forms (-*s*, -*ed*, -*ing*) of words already on the list are not listed separately, but the endings are given in parenthesis after the word.

5	Mabel		cousins		took
	was		played		away
	a		they		from
	whale		swam		to
	she		too		place
	live(d)	**7**	one		called
	in		day		Marineland
	the		some	**9**	fish
	Pacific		men		and
	Ocean		came		sea
	water		ship		animals
	very		caught		big
	deep		did		pools
	blue		not		or
6	happy		hurt		tanks
	with		put		people
	her	**8**	then		come

	see		knew		crane
	all		that		many
10	into		told		mattresses
	small		how		raft
	at		help	21	lifted
	could	15	cool	22	truck
	hide		cream	23	fifty
	it		for		feet
11	sun		an		up
	shone		old		air
	down		bag		new
	hot		over	24	gave
	top		now		shots
	fin	16	feel		were
	under		any		whale-sized
	so		better		kept
	burn(ed)		even		quiet
12	looked		stopped		until
	through		eating		got
	liked		everyone		used
	glass		wanted	25	made
	but		thought		man
13	unhappy		what		walked
	sad		do		around
	lay	17	had		get
	on		idea		know
	bottom		there	26	felt
	of		round		covered
	still		if		shine
	soon		move(d)	27	before
	sick		would		long
14	doctor		have		blew
	he		more		spray
	head	18	be		because
	tail		easy		well
19	saw	19	last		again
	sunburned		brought		

The Follett BEGINNING-TO-READ Books

Purpose of the Beginning-to-Read Books: To provide easy-to-read materials that will appeal to the interests of primary children. Careful attention is given to vocabulary load and sentence length, but the first criterion is interest to children.

Reading Levels: These books are written at three reading levels, indicated by one, two, or three dots beneath the *Beginning-to-Read* symbol on the back cover. *Level One* books can be read by first grade children in the last half of the school year. As children increase their reading ability they will be able to enjoy *Level Two* books. And as they grow further in their reading ability they will progress to *Level Three* books. Some first grade children will read *Level Two* and *Level Three* books. Many third graders, and even some fourth graders, will read and enjoy *Level One* and *Level Two* books, as well as *Level Three* books. The range of interest of *Beginning-to-Read* books stretches far beyond their reading level.

Use of the Beginning-to-Read Books: Because of their high interest and readability, these books are ideal for independent reading by primary children—at school, in the library, and at home. The books may also be incorporated into the basic reading program to develop children's interests, expand their vocabularies, and improve word-attack skills. It has been suggested that they might serve as the foundation for a skillfully directed reading program. Many *Beginning-to-Read* books correlate with the social studies, science, and other subject fields. All will help children grow in the language arts. Children will read the *Beginning-to-Read* books with confidence, with success, and with real enjoyment.